A business tool kit with eve[r]
you need to set up a small b[usi]ness

To Vicki,

YOUR
BUSINESS
CUBE

*Thanks for your support.
I hope you find this
useful. Amanda
x*

AMANDA CULLEN

Amanda Cullen © Copyright 2020

The right of Amanda Cullen to be identified as the author of this work has been asserted by her in accordance with the Copyright, Designs and Patents Act 1988.

All rights reserved.

No reproduction, copy or transmission of this publication may be made without express prior written permission. No paragraph of this publication may be reproduced, copied or transmitted except with express prior written permission or in accordance with the provisions of the Copyright Act 1956 (as amended). Any person who commits any unauthorised act in relation to this publication may be liable to criminal prosecution and civil claims for damage.

The author and publisher do not accept any responsibility for any loss, which may arise as a consequence of reliance on information contained in this book.

Published by Goldcrest Books International Ltd
www.goldcrestbooks.com
publish@goldcrestbooks.com

ISBN: 978-1-913719-22-7
eISBN: 978-1-913719-23-4

Reviews

"I really enjoyed reading *Your Business Cube*. The structure, objectives and clarity are excellent and there is a professional, warm and friendly tone, which gives a true sense of the author behind the words.

I think this will be a great business aid:

- for start-ups, where addressing the questions on values and 'who you are' are vital
- for more experienced businesses, where the latter sections of the book will be particularly useful."

Forbes Low
CEO, Kingston Chamber of Commerce

"I've read a few books since starting my business and this is definitely my favourite. It's helped me more with my business than any others. Everything is really clear."

Rachael Dalton
Virtual PA

"The wonderfully simple structure of this business workbook is so effective: the Why, the What and the How broken down into 3 focus points with 3 exercises in each.

It's approachable (even fun!) sometimes really challenging (in a good, self-examination way) and it's practical – thank you.

Really good for start-ups but also an invaluable review tool for SME owners and their teams at any stage."

Caroline Barraclough
Owner, Caz Bookkeeping

"I really enjoyed this book – it was easy to follow and had simple instructions for each task. Having spaces to complete the exercises in the book as I went along was particularly useful."

Rina Bailey
Owner, Dotty's Oils

"This book is packed full of foundational elements that need to be in place for a business to work well in the long-term. It brings together these elements clearly in blocks, with practical exercises to help the business owner drive out clarity!

I would have loved to have this book by my side when starting my business."

Joanna Gaudoin
Owner, Inside Out Image

Contents

Introduction

Welcome to Your Business Cube.

"What IS a business cube?" I hear you ask.

It's my simple model to describe the structure of this book, and a good way to think about the structure of your business, too.

There are three main sections – Why, What and How.

In each section there are **three** topics.

For each topic there are **three** exercises.

This gives you a 3 x 3 x 3 Business Cube: 27 exercises to help you run a successful business!

Together, we're going to assemble Your Business Cube.

If you are just starting out in business, this book will prove an essential tool to give you clarity on what you want to achieve with your business, and how to go about it. All the elements that we cover are key to creating a strong foundation for your business.

If you've been running your business for a while, this book will give you a great opportunity to take stock and identify where you need to increase your focus.

I recommend that you work through it now, and then revisit it every year to remind yourself of what you set out to do, check in with your progress, and make any adjustments you feel necessary – either to your plans if these have changed, or to your business if it has veered off track without you noticing.

Some of the exercises must be done alone, but others lend themselves to optional participation from others.

I have marked these exercises with a ★. If, as time goes on, you start to build a team around you, whether that's staff or regular suppliers or advisers, you may want to involve them.

I strongly believe in keeping things simple.

I wrote this book to make it simpler for you to run your business successfully, whether you are just starting out or need a reboot to make the most of the business you already have.

I've therefore deliberately made the format of this book simple too. It's a quick help guide that you can work through now and refer back to whenever you need it.

I hope you find it straightforward and simple to follow, and that it takes your business from strength to strength.

What's behind the Business Cube thinking?

I believe that there are three key questions that every business owner should address in order to be successful. I talk about them a lot. They underpin my coaching and my workshops, and nearly every conversation that I have with business owners.

If you know your answers to these three questions you will be well on your way to business success. If you don't, your business may do fine for a while, but I suspect that at some stage it will suffer from the lack of a firm foundation.

So, what are the three magic questions? Here we go.

> **Why** do you want to run your own business and why THIS business?

> **What** does your business look like and what do you need to make it work?

> **How** are you going to make your business work for you?

Big businesses would probably talk about mission statements, corporate vision and strategy. They might also talk about corporate values. These are fancy words for exactly the same thing.

I like to keep things simple – I hate jargon. But if you want to describe the answers to my three magic questions as your Purpose, Vision and Strategy, go ahead!

How to use this book

I know that many business owners are rule breakers.

Often it's why you don't want to work for someone else, or why you're convinced that you can make your great idea into a business.

So, I'm not going to say that you MUST work through this book in order.

I do, however, RECOMMEND that you work through the book broadly in order, because each section provides a building block for the next.

That said, if there is an exercise that you can't complete right now, or that simply doesn't resonate with you, feel free to skip over it and carry on. You can always come back to revisit it later.

You will find some of these exercises easy, and I encourage you to dig deeper than your first response as you may find some unexpected learning emerges from doing so.

Each section follows the same format, which is in three parts.

First is an explanation of the question. This is where I tell you what the topic is and why it's important.

Second is a set of three exercises related to the topic. They are designed to help you work out your answers to the question (which, incidentally, will be different from the answers that anyone else reading this book will come up with). There is space for you to put your answers in the book so that you have everything in one place. Of course, if you prefer to use a separate notebook – go right ahead!

Third is an invitation for you to note your learnings, with some prompts in case you need them. It's entirely up to you how – or indeed whether – you use this section. I've included it as I know some people like to have all their notes in one place.

Why?

Why do you want to run your own business and why THIS business?

Sometimes I hear people say: "I want to run my own business" or "I want to be an entrepreneur". That's fine, as far as it goes, but any old business just won't do. You need to identify the perfect business for you, the one that fits you like a glove and that you can't imagine NOT having.

Why is this important?

As a business owner, it's critical that you really care about your business. Otherwise it's all very well on the good days, but a real struggle on the bad.

The following exercises are designed to help you get clearer on three aspects of your Why? – your values, your strengths and your 'must haves'.

1. Why do you need to know and understand your values?

Your values are the elements in life that matter to you, and your combination of values is unique to you. It will be different to everyone else around you, although some people will probably share some of your values to some degree.

When your life gives you the opportunity to satisfy these values, it is much more enjoyable and fulfilling, so it follows that you'll want to ensure that your business gives you this opportunity.

You can think of values in two groups. The first is the set of values that keep you grounded and ensure that you have a solid foundation. They are core to your wellbeing and for that reason you may like to think of them as your CORE values.

The second set of values are the ones that energise you and make you feel great. They are the values that can drive you forward and support you to take bold steps. For that reason, you may like to think of them as your INSPIRING values.

There is a difference between the values that are intrinsic to you and those that society imposes on you.

For example: punctuality and timeliness are more important in some cultures than in others. If they are not values for you then you will typically make an effort to 'comply' with the local approach simply because it is expected of you.

If, on the other hand, they are your own values then you will typically always be on time, and get frustrated by others who aren't.

When you know what your values are you can work to ensure that the business you build satisfies those values.

Exercise 1 – identifying your values

Write down everything you can think of that gives you a sense of satisfaction or fulfilment, fires you up, makes you feel grounded or secure. Areas to explore include:

- Relationships, e.g. family, friends, community, love, friendship, connection.
- Activities, e.g. hobbies, sport, intellectual pursuits, adventure, challenge, learning.

- Environments, e.g. nature, urban spaces, water, mountains, woods, beauty.
- Qualities, e.g. punctuality, compassion, respect, loyalty.

Relationships	
Activities	
Environments	
Qualities	
Other	

You can also do an online search for 'values checklist', which will give you a wealth of suggested values to consider. However, it's better to do this after you have created your own initial list. Otherwise you may miss out elements that are very personal to you and not included on suggested lists.

Once you have complied your list, put it away for a couple of days. Then get it out again, review it and see whether everything still resonates, or whether there is anything else you want to add. We are often affected by our emotions at the time of compiling the list, so taking a second look helps to counteract this and give you a more balanced result.

Exercise 2 – noticing emotions

Over the next 7 days, notice when you feel a strong emotion: excitement, love, pride, anger, upset, frustration, etc. Later in the day, when the emotion has cooled, go back and reflect on what caused it.

If it was a negative emotion, it's likely that a CORE value was being trampled on. Try to uncover that value and if it's not already there, add it to the list you created in Exercise 1.

If it was a positive emotion, it's likely that an INSPIRING value is being satisfied. Try to identify what it is that inspires you and if it's not already there, add it to the list you created in Exercise 1.

Exercise 3 – prioritising key values

Looking at your list, identify the 5 values that are MOST important to you. What could you absolutely not live without? How do these values show up in your everyday life now, and how can you ensure they will be satisfied as you build your business?

1.
2.
3.
4.
5.

Learning to take forward

What do you want to capture from these three exercises? Remember that the goal is to make sure that your business is aligned with your values rather than in conflict with them.

Use this page to make some notes.

2. Why do you need to know and play to your strengths?

We all have things we are naturally good at and others we find harder. Nobody is good at everything.

For the purposes of this exercise we will call things we are good at our STRENGTHS and those we find harder our WEAKNESSES. Some of these we were born with and others will have developed throughout our lives and become stronger or weaker as a consequence of where our focus has been placed, and what external influences have been brought to bear on them.

There is a difference between STRENGTHS and skills. Strengths come naturally to us whereas skills are learned.

For example, we may be naturally good at numbers and have used that strength to develop the skills of being a whizz with spreadsheets. We can still learn to use spreadsheets effectively even if numbers aren't a strength, but it's less likely that we'll feel comfortable doing it.

When we run our own business, it makes sense to give ourselves every opportunity to succeed. This means we should focus firmly on our STRENGTHS and make maximum use of them. We shouldn't beat ourselves up about our WEAKNESSES but find ways to minimise their impact on our business.

First of all, though, we need to know and understand our strengths.

Exercise 1 – listing known strengths

Make a list of everything you know you are good at. If you find this difficult, think about different areas of your life and identify which activities came naturally to you, or you found easy.

Areas to explore include:

- Your childhood.
- Your school days.
- Your first job.
- Other jobs or voluntary roles.
- Other groups, e.g. sports, music, hobbies.

Childhood	
School days	
First job	
Jobs / roles	
Other	

Exercise 2 – asking others for input

Often, we struggle to identify our strengths because if we find something easy, we assume everyone else does too! Asking others to tell us what we are good at may feel uncomfortable, but it can really shine a light on strengths you didn't know you had.

So, ask 5–10 people who know you well what they consider your top 3 strengths are. These could be family members, current or former colleagues, or friends.

List the 15–30 answers they give you and identify which answers occur more than once. Remember that people may use slightly different words to describe the same strength, so group these together.

Use the table on the next page to write your answers.

Any answer that occurs three or more times will indicate a tip-top strength, and anything that occurs more than once is also worth noting.

Friend / family	Strength 1	Strength 2	Strength 3
1			
2			
3			
4			
5			
(6)			
(7)			
(8)			
(9)			
(10)			

Exercise 3 – categorising strengths

Just because we have a strength in a particular area it doesn't automatically mean that we enjoy exercising that strength. When we're building our business we want to maximise our use of the strengths that will bring us enjoyment and satisfaction.

Look at your list of strengths and separate them into two groups: things you enjoy, or get pleasure or satisfaction from, and things that you don't particularly enjoy.

For example, feedback from Exercise 2 may indicate that you are a great organiser, and if you love organising, that's a positive strength. Or it may indicate that you're a great speaker, and if you love speaking and presenting, that's a positive strength.

But if you hate organising things, and despite being good at it you would much rather rely on someone else to do it, then you are unlikely to build your business around a service to others that involves organising them, such as project management or virtual administration.

And if you hate speaking in public you may still do some of it, for example introducing yourself at networking events, but you are unlikely to develop a career as a public speaker, or make that a key element of either your offering or the way you promote it.

Don't worry if you have no negative / neutral strengths. That's absolutely fine.

Positive Strengths	Negative/Neutral Strengths

Learning to take forward

What do you want to capture from these three exercises? Remember that the goal is to make sure that you can use your strengths to their best advantage in your business.

Use this page to make some notes.

3. Why do you need to be clear on your 'must haves'?

Your 'must haves' are the things that you must have in your business in order for it to satisfy your needs. These are not the same as your values but may include some of them.

For example, your personal circumstances might mean that you MUST HAVE flexibility to work around other time constraints such as school terms. Perhaps you have health issues that will restrict how much work you can do in any one day, or how much physical effort can be involved.

Your financial circumstances might mean that you cannot avoid any significant outlay to set up your business, or that you MUST HAVE a certain amount of money coming in as quickly as possible.

Or your emotional needs might mean that you need a significant amount of company or solitude in order to function effectively, and that you MUST HAVE people around you, or conversely space to work alone.

Exercise 1 – understanding situational needs

Identify what, if any, 'must haves' arise from your personal circumstances.

Are there any constraints on your time, e.g. from childcare needs, caring responsibilities, household responsibilities or from other paid or unpaid work that you are committed to continuing?

If so, how many hours per day, week or month can you realistically commit to your business?

If you need flexibility, how flexible do you need to be?

Can you commit to certain times or days? Or do you need to be able to drop everything and then pick it up again later?

(This will affect the kind of business model you need.)

Are there any constraints on your health, e.g. from a disability or chronic illness that limits what you can do, or how much energy you have?

What does this mean you need to factor into your business model?

Make a list of any 'must haves' you have identified, and the implications for your business.

Must Haves	Implications

Exercise 2 – assessing financial needs

Make a list of your monthly outgoings. A good way of doing this is to look back at your bank and credit card transactions over three months and take the monthly average of your spending. Then add in 1/12 of any annual bills that may not occur in those three months.

Then divide this into two parts:

- Essential spend, e.g. mortgage, energy bills, rates, council tax, loan repayments, food shopping, essential clothes and household shopping, travel costs.

- Optional spend, e.g. take-aways, entertainment, alcohol, clubs, savings, charity donations, holidays.

Essential spend item	Cost	Optional spend item	Cost
Total:			

Now consider the following questions:

i. Are you going to be 100% reliant financially on your business, or do you want it to supplement other household income (yours or someone else's)?

ii. How long can you survive without any income from your business, taking into account other income or savings?

iii. How much monthly income will you need from the business once the period described in ii has passed?

Reliance?	
Survival period?	
Monthly income needed?	

Exercise 3 – recognising emotional needs

Identify what you need to support a good emotional state. For this you may want to look back at your values, as they often provide a clue to what's important.

i. How important is community – having others around you some or most of the time, and how close does your relationship with them need to be? For example, if you need to be with others, would working in a communal space satisfy your needs? Or do you need to be part of a team working together? Or would having customers that you meet and interact with be sufficient?

ii. How important is environment – i.e. your surroundings? This may be largely determined by the nature of your business, but consider whether you prefer to be in town or country, inland or by water, indoors or in nature. Think also about your immediate surroundings. What does your workspace / office ideally need to be like to make you feel your best?

iii. How important is movement? We all need some exercise to function at our best, but if you are very active then a business that is 100% desk-based may not be ideal for you.

For each of these, mark where you feel you sit on the line from Unimportant to Essential.

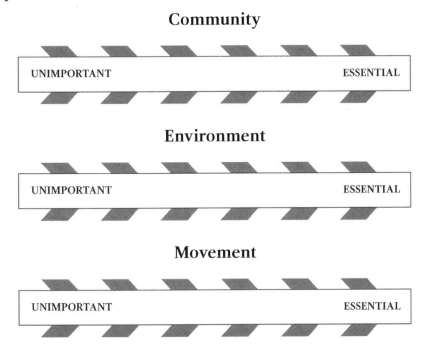

Community

UNIMPORTANT   ESSENTIAL

Environment

UNIMPORTANT   ESSENTIAL

Movement

UNIMPORTANT   ESSENTIAL

Learning to take forward

What do you want to capture from these three exercises? Remember that the goal is to make sure that your business fully satisfies your 'must haves'.

Use this page to make some notes.

What?

What does your business look like and what do you need to make it work?

In this section we look at three key aspects of your business that I believe are fundamental to being successful.

You need to know what the product or service is that you are going to sell, and you need to know who you are going to sell it to. These two elements are obviously critical.

The third element is sometimes overlooked, but I think it's really important. You need to know what your goal is for the business: what you want to achieve with your business, and by when.

The following exercises are designed to help you get clearer on three aspects of your What? – your offering, your market and your goal.

1. What are you selling?

For any business to be successful you need to have an offering – something to sell that other people want to buy. This can be a product or a service.

It's important to understand your offering really well. This will help you position and price it correctly.

★ Exercise 1 – understanding customer needs

Everything we buy responds to one or more of four basic requirements. These are:

- a Problem
- a Pain
- a Desire, and
- a Need

(You will find that I refer to these four requirements frequently, often using the acronym, PPDN.)

For example:

If you sell luxury beauty products, they might solve the problem of what to buy the person who has everything.

If you sell sports massage services, they might tackle the pain of an athlete's injury.

If you sell home-made food, then depending on what it is, it might satisfy the customer's desire for something sweet and indulgent to eat – or their need for a nutritious ready-meal for the family.

What is the problem, pain, desire or need that your offering will address? **Write it down here.**

★ Exercise 2 – understanding the competition

It's important to understand why your customers will buy from you rather than from someone else. If they didn't buy from you, where else might they go to address their problem, pain, desire or need?

Start by identifying and making a list of your main competitors. These could be people who sell or do something similar to you, or they might sell or do something quite different that responds to the same problem, pain, desire or need. You may want to identify a generic group or a named business.

For example, if you are a physiotherapist, your list might include: other physiotherapists, osteopaths, chiropractors, massage therapists, or it might specifically name someone who works in the same field and geographical location as you do.

If you are a nanny, your list might include: other nannies, childminders, grandparents and nurseries.

If you sell luxury hand-made soap, your list might include: other niche soap retailers, pharmacies, supermarkets, high street beauty stores, beauty salons, etc.

Think about what might attract someone to each of these competitors. For example, reputation / brand, price, tried-and-tested results, easy access, etc.

Competitors	Why buy from them?

★ Exercise 3 – differentiating yourself

What makes you different? In order to attract customers, you need to first get clear, and then communicate, what makes you different from your competitors.

Consider the following:

Your personality: how do you relate to your customers? For example, are you calm or energetic, gentle or forceful, chatty or quiet? Do you build strong relationships easily, or are you more reserved and private?

Your style: how do you approach your work? For example, are you structure and process-oriented, spontaneous and flexible, creative and intuitive, data and research driven, or ...?

Your strengths: what are you good at that has made you choose to have this kind of business? Refer back to the list of strengths that you made on pages 10–11.

Your expertise: what training and qualifications (if any) do you have that equip you to run your business?

Your experience: what have you done that equips you perfectly for your business? This might be previous paid work or other life experience, like being captain of a sports team, raising a family, caring for a sick relative, or volunteering.

Your offering: what are you offering that is unique or different from what others offer to meet an equivalent problem, pain, desire or need (or what aspect of it is unique or different)?

Personality	
Style	
Strengths	
Expertise	
Experience	
Offering	

Then consider which of these could make you a more attractive choice than each of the competitors above.

Revisit the list in the previous exercise to complete this exercise.

Competitors	Why buy from me instead?

Learning to take forward

What do you want to capture from these three exercises? Remember that the goal is to make sure that your offering is really clear and meets a specific need of some kind.

Use this page to make some notes.

2. What's your market?

However good your product or service, you will only have a successful business if you sell something that people want to buy!

So, it's important to be really clear who your offering is aimed at.

Many new business owners start out thinking they can help EVERYBODY! They imagine that the more potential customers they have, the more successful they will be.

Wrong! In fact, the more targeted or niche your product is, the more you will stand out from the crowd and attract exactly the right customers.

In the previous section you uncovered the problem, pain, desire or need (PPDN) that would lead someone to buy from you. Now it's time to explore who is likely to have that problem, pain, desire or need.

The best way to really understand your ideal customer is to create a clear picture, or 'avatar' of that person.

A word about the use of 'customer' and 'client': many people who sell a service prefer to talk about clients, whereas if you sell a product you are more likely to talk about customers. It really doesn't matter. Both words describe the person who buys what you have to offer.

For the purposes of this book, we'll use the word customer.

Exercise 1 – storytelling

Visit a busy place – café, pub, shopping centre – or if that's not practical, go channel-hopping to spot different people on TV, or explore YouTube or Instagram. Or you can flick through magazines if you prefer.

As you look at the people, ask yourself: who would be a great customer?

Spot someone who you imagine would be your ideal customer. Then build a story about them, including:

> their name, age, gender, ethnicity, marital status;

> their personal circumstances, e.g. family, job or role, where they live;

> their personality – quiet or outgoing, nervous or confident, stylish or plain, etc.;

> their interests – where they shop, what they do in their spare time, what they read, watch and listen to;

> their spending power.

Pay particular attention to any interests that are relevant to your offering, for example, fashion if your offering is fashion-related, or sport if your offering is related to that.

Get really clear on this person. It may take you a little while but keep thinking about them as you go about your business over the next day or so and keep asking yourself, "would they do this or like this?" Add your answer to your story.

Capture your story here.

Exercise 2 – clarifying your ideal customer

In the first storytelling exercise you in fact created your customer avatar, but not everyone who fits that description will be a great customer. It's really useful to have a sense of who your best and worst customers are likely to be.

If you have already had customers, you can think about these. If not, you'll need to imagine what a best and worst customer might look like.

Here are three questions to ask yourself. Think first about your best customer and then about your worst. The same questions apply to both.

i. What is their Problem, Pain, Desire or Need and (if you serve businesses rather than consumers) their industry or sector?

ii. What kind of personality do they have (easy to deal with, fun, challenging, thoughtful, direct, awkward, grumpy, moaning, etc.)?

iii. What is their attitude to you – and to paying for your service or product?

	Best	Worst
PPDN / Industry		
Personality		
Attitude		

What does this tell you about who to seek out and who to avoid? Write your thoughts in the box below.

★ Exercise 3 – finding customers

In order to find customers, you need to be visible where they are, whether or not they are actively looking for what you offer.

So, thinking about your ideal customer, where might you find them?

Start with how you can reach them either directly or through existing contacts. Who do you know that might either be an ideal customer themselves, or know others who could be?

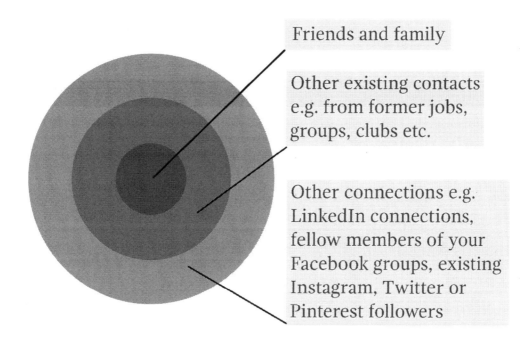

Friends and family

Other existing contacts e.g. from former jobs, groups, clubs etc.

Other connections e.g. LinkedIn connections, fellow members of your Facebook groups, existing Instagram, Twitter or Pinterest followers

Also think about physical places your customer might lurk, e.g. doctors' surgeries, local offices, school playgrounds, cafés and coffee shops, bars, etc.

Which social media platform(s) is your ideal customer most likely to use regularly? Write your answers on the next page.

Friends and family	
Existing contacts	
Other connections	
Physical Places	
Social media	

Learning to take forward

What do you want to capture from these three exercises? Remember that the goal is to get a really clear understanding of who will buy your product or service.

Use this page to make some notes.

3. What's your goal?

Some people question the need to have a specific goal for their business. Think of it like a journey.

When you leave home to go somewhere you always have a destination in mind, don't you? You're going to the shops, to meet someone, to visit a museum, gym, pub, etc. And because you know where you're going, you know what route to take, which bus or train to catch, or which road to walk or drive down.

If you didn't know where you were going, you would simply hop on and off buses or trains at a whim, or drive or wander aimlessly, potentially going around in circles.

It's the same with your business journey. In order to move forward and make progress, you need to know where you're heading.

It's also useful to have a timeline in mind. Going back to your trip to the shops, if you have unlimited time you might walk; if you're in a hurry you might jump in the car. With your business, if you want to achieve your goal quickly, you'll need to take more assertive and bold action than if you are happy to take time to build the business up.

Your goal could focus on one of a number of aspects of your business. For example, it could be:

- Financial (double your turnover, earn £x,000, reach VAT threshold).

- Geographical (expand across county, country, continent, globally).

- Workforce (grow to 3/5/10 staff).

- Product / service range (add 1,3,10 to range, diversify into x other market).

- Product / service reach (sell x000 products, help y people).

- Reputation (become the number 1 business in your area / region / world).

Different goal-setting exercises work for different people. Take a look at the three below and decide which one appeals most and do that first. However, I suggest you also try the other two, as stretching yourself in unfamiliar ways can uncover ideas that you might not otherwise have thought of.

★ Exercise 1 – creative brainstorming

Get a large sheet of paper, or a white board and some coloured pens.

Set a timer for 3 minutes

Ask yourself this question: "What do I want from my business?"

Then write down everything that occurs to you in 3 minutes. Don't filter it or stop to review. At this stage, any and every word or idea that comes up is equally valid.

If you're still going after 3 minutes, carry on, but don't stop earlier.

When you've finished, put down your pens, step away and go and have a cup of coffee or a short walk.

Then come back and take a fresh look at what you have written.

Put a circle around any words that jump out and really resonate.

Start to craft a sentence that expresses what you want from your business.

Don't worry if it's not perfect! You don't have to get it right first time.

Exercise 2 – quiet contemplation

Set aside some time when you won't be disturbed. I suggest allowing at least an hour.

Go somewhere that you find inspiring. Depending on your personal preference, this could be a calm, beautiful place such as a garden, wood, or by the river or sea. Alternatively, it could be an exciting, vibrant place like a city centre, by a modern piece of architecture or even a room in your home.

Take a few moments to look outward and appreciate the inspiration around you. Really soak it up with your eyes, ears, nose and touch.

Now turn your attention inward and ask yourself this question: "What do I want from my business?"

Sit, stand or walk quietly, letting this question hang in the air.

Notice what words come up for you.

Then find somewhere where you can sit and capture what you have uncovered.

Start to craft a sentence that expresses what you want from your business.

Don't worry if it's not perfect! You don't have to get it right first time.

Exercise 3 – creating a vision board

A vision board is any sort of board on which you display images that represent whatever you want to be, do or have in your life.

You just need a large sheet of paper, magazines, scissors, and glue, and maybe some pens.

Step 1: Take a few moments to focus on your business. Think about your values, your product / service, your customers and your aspirations.

Step 2: Cut or tear out images from the magazines. These can be pictures or words.

Step 3: Go through the images and begin to lay your favourites on the board. Eliminate any images that no longer feel right. This step is where your intuition comes in. As you lay the pictures on the board, you'll get a sense how the board should be laid out.

Step 4: Glue everything onto the board. Add writing if you want.

Step 5: (optional, but powerful) Leave space in the very centre of the vision board for a fantastic photo of yourself where you look radiant and happy. Paste yourself in the centre of your board.

Put your vision board where you will see it every day. It is in focusing on your images that they stay in your mind and help you move towards them.

Start to craft a sentence that expresses what you want from your business.

Don't worry if it's not perfect! You don't have to get it right first time.

Write your answers on the following page.

If you are technology minded, you can also create a vision board online, using something like Pinterest. Make sure before you start compiling it to follow Step 1 above – take time to focus on your business. Think about your values, your product / service, your customers and your aspirations.

Learning to take forward

What do you want to capture from these three exercises? Remember that the purpose of your goal is to make sure that you know where you are heading with your business, and what's important to you.

Use this page to make some notes.

How?

How are you going to make your business work for you?

In this section we look at some of the practicalities you need to consider in order to make your business successful.

You need to know how much to charge for your product or service, how (and where) to sell it and how to manage all the different hats that you wear as a business owner (producer, administrator, marketing manager, finance manager, social media whizz, etc.).

The following exercises are designed to help you get clearer on three aspects of your How? – your pricing, your marketing and your overall business management.

1. How will you price it?

Understanding how much you can, and should, charge for your offering is important. It's something that many people struggle with, either overcharging or, more often, undercharging.

(Note: this section does not address how much you need to earn. We considered that on page 13 in the 'must haves' section. However, once you have worked through the exercises in this section you should review whether your costs and your pricing are realistically likely to generate the income you need. If not, something has to change!)

It can be easier to price a product than a service, because you should be able to accurately identify how much it costs to make, and then it's a question of considering the cost of marketing it and the profit margin you can realistically expect.

It's usually harder to market a service because there are fewer, if any, raw materials. Instead you are selling expertise, understanding of the customer's need, and time.

It's also important to be clear where you want to position yourself in your marketplace, as the second exercise below explains.

In this section I have assumed you only have one product or service. That's the most common way for businesses to start out. Of course, if you offer two or more different products or services then the exercise will be more complicated as you'll need to do it for each one.

If you can't identify your development and marketing costs for each offering separately then you'll need to calculate them as a whole, and then make an educated guess as to how to proportion them.

★ Exercise 1 – understanding costs

I like to split costs into three groups: production costs, development costs and marketing costs.

There is in fact a fourth cost – your time spent working on your business. However, for now we're going to keep things simple and focus on the other three.

The approach you take will differ depending on whether you have a product or a service, so I have created two separate sections for the rest of this exercise. Make sure that you choose the correct one for your business.

Product

For your production costs, you'll need to take into account your raw materials, plus the cost of turning them into the end product, which may involve the hire or purchase of equipment, or paying someone else to do the process.

Start by listing all the elements that go into making your products and the associated cost. Depending on what you sell, it may be easy to identify the cost per item, but it's likely to be more practical to calculate the cost per 100 or per 1,000 items, in which case you'll then need to divide your answer by 100 or 1,000 to arrive at a cost per item.

The more accurate you can be the better, but don't despair or give up on this exercise if you have to make an educated guess at some parts.

Now consider your development costs. What did you spend on developing the product to the point where it is ready to sell? You need to recoup these too before you can start to consider that you are making a profit, but how quickly you can do so will depend how much they are, how many products you can sell, and how expensive your product is.

Decide how much it is realistic to add to the production cost per item. For example, if your development costs are £1,000 you may want to add 10p to the production cost per item, which will assume you recoup development costs after the first 10,000 sales.

Finally, consider your marketing costs. If you're just starting out then you may not know what these will be yet, but remember that every pound you spend on networking, or advertising, or getting business cards or flyers printed, will contribute to your costs and reduce your profit.

Product elements	Development costs	Production costs	Marketing costs
Total cost per item			
Cost per individual Item			

Service

For a service, the term 'production costs' doesn't resonate so well. You are highly likely to effectively be selling your service by the hour, so there's a temptation to think you are simply selling your time.

Surprisingly, however, selling your time may in fact include costs that we can classify as 'production'.

For example:

- Do you use premises and or have utility bills that have to be paid for, even if it's just a room in your home with associated energy bills, or your IT and phone?

- Do you wear specialist clothes that have to be bought or set aside for work?

- Do you have to pay for childcare to free you up to do your work?

- Do you need stationery, such as pens, paper, printer paper, folders, to support the administration of your business?

Decide whether you are going to calculate these costs on a monthly or quarterly basis. Then divide that by 4 or by 13 to get a weekly cost.

I suggest a weekly cost because it's then easy to see how much money you must make each week. If you're charging your service by the hour (as most do when starting out) then once you know how much you're going to charge, you'll know how many paid hours you need to do to cover your costs.

Once you are clear on these production costs you need to factor in development costs.

These will include any of the following:

- Training courses.
- Design costs.

- Cost of infrastructure such as machinery, premises, materials, laptop, printer, phone.

You need to recoup these too before you can start to consider that you are making a profit, but how quickly you can do so will depend how much they are, how much paid work you do and how expensive your service is.

For example, if your development costs are £5,000 you might aim to recoup them over 5 years, which means that you'll need to add £1,000 / 52 or approximately £20 per week to your costs.

Finally, consider your marketing costs. If you're just starting out then you may not know what these will be yet, but remember that every pound you spend on networking, or advertising, or getting business cards or flyers printed, will contribute to your costs and reduce your profit.

Product elements	Development costs	Production costs	Marketing costs
Total			
Cost per week			

Exercise 2 – positioning your offering

It's important to be clear where you want to position yourself in the market. Think back to the 'What's Your Market?' exercises earlier in the book and be clear where you will find your ideal customer.

For example, if you were selling clothes, consider whether you would be aiming at:

- The Primark market – rock bottom prices to appeal to the mass market.

- The John Lewis market – good value prices to appeal to the middle market.

- The Gucci market – top prices to appeal to the high-end market.

To use another example, if you were selling cars, consider whether you would be aiming at:

- The Dacia market.

- The Toyota market.

- The Rolls Royce market.

Mark where you want to sit on the spectrum from mass market to luxury.

What are the implications of this for your pricing? If you are aiming for mass market, you will probably need to cut your costs and profit margin to the bone and aim for high volumes to make money.

Conversely, if you are aiming towards the luxury end of the market, your focus will be on quality and value, creating a fantastic, and possibly more tailored, experience for a smaller number of customers.

★ Exercise 3 – valuing your work

Pricing is not just a matter of covering your costs (see first exercise above) and adding a margin for profit.

Knowing where you want to position yourself in the market (Exercise 2) will help you understand where you should be pitching your pricing.

Work through these questions to help you understand what you should consider when setting your prices.

i.   Where else can people get what you offer or an alternative solution to their problem, pain, desire or need (PPDN)?

ii.   What would that cost?

iii. What makes your product or service different / better?

iv.   Reality check – what is the spending power of your target market?

Alternative for their PPDN?	
Cost?	
Your difference	
Reality check	

If you are selling a service, you may also want to ask these questions to help understand the value you bring.

    v.   What skills are involved in producing your services?

    vi.   What training have you had?

    vii.   What 'life learning' has contributed to the way you offer your services?

Skills?	
Training?	
Life learning?	

Also consider this key question:

What is the value of my offering to my customer – i.e. how big is their problem, pain, desire or need (PPDN), and what is it worth to them to get it sorted?

Write your answers in the box provided on the next page.

Learning to take forward

What do you want to capture from these three exercises? Remember that the goal is to set your prices at a level that takes into account all the costs involved (including costs that you may have incurred sometime in the past) and has an additional allowance on top to give you some profit.

Use this page to make some notes.

2. How will you market it?

In order for your business to be successful you need people to know about what you sell, and for that you need to think about your marketing.

Marketing is NOT selling. It is positioning your offering in the marketplace and raising brand awareness, so that people know what you stand for.

Marketing starts with strategy. You need to be clear what messages you want to give out about your business, and who your audience is.

Once you know what messages you want to give out, you can think about how you do it both online (e.g. emails, website, social media, blogs, newsletters, advertising) and offline (e.g. word of mouth, business cards, flyers, posters, banners, magazine articles).

Exercise 1 – setting objectives

Decide on your objective, i.e. what do you want to achieve with your marketing?

For example: you may want to:

- Raise awareness of your existence.

- Get your name known more widely in a geographical area or by a particular group of people with specific needs or wants.

- Help people understand what you do.

- Demonstrate expertise.

- Help people get to know who you are and what you stand for.

It's OK to have a single objective or a combination. For example, you may want to build your reputation as an expert in your field and help people get to know you better.

Your objective(s) may change from time to time or from marketing activity to activity, but remember that it's always the first thing you should think about.

So right now, thinking about your overall business, what's your main marketing objective?

★ Exercise 2 – identifying your approach

Get clear on your approach to your marketing. This comprises two key elements:

Style: this must be consistent with everything else you do: For example, your style could be: classic, quirky, serious, playful, plain, colourful, etc.

If you have already done your website, or started promoting your business on social media, then you'll probably have a good sense of this. If not, then a good way to start to develop it is to look at other brands and see what you like and don't like. Think back to your values too, as they may inform your style.

Tone: again consistency is key. It's important that you sound like you. What kind of tone best conveys who you are and what you stand for? For example, you could be: authoritative, friendly, caring, questioning, formal, casual, etc.

If you're not sure how you are perceived, ask!

Ask friends, other business owners you may have met via networking, or any customers you already have, what words come up when they think about you.

Style	Tone

Exercise 3 – digging deeper

For each piece of marketing activity, you will need to address three things:

    i.   Content: the key messages that you want to get across. Remember back to your objective and avoid trying to sell your product or service. Think instead about how you want your offering to make your customer feel. What's the emotion that you want to trigger in them?

    ii.   Frequency: is this a one-off exercise or a series of communications? You need to think about what will sit comfortably with your audience – AND you need to be realistic about what you can commit to, both in terms of your time and, if relevant, money.

    iii.   Format: how you are going to package your marketing, e.g. email, talk, flyer, social media post, blog, advert. Don't forget to think about your ideal customer and where you will find them.

Capture some thoughts here.

Marketing is a massive topic and in a book like this we can only scratch the surface. However, these three exercises should give you a good start. To explore it more you could:

- Like and follow marketing specialists, or social media experts on social media, visit their websites and sign up to their newsletters.

- Look out for 5-day or 30-day challenges on a whole range of topics from posting more varied content on social media, to blogging, to writing newsletters, to speaking confidently. You can Google these or spot them being offered by those same marketing specialists and experts.

- Browse the shelves of your local or online book shop where there are masses of books about marketing!

Learning to take forward

What do you want to capture from these three exercises? Remember that the goal is to determine your approach to marketing so that you can build awareness of who you are and what you stand for.

Use this page to make some notes.

3. How will you manage it?

When you start out you may want to keep your business simple and the idea of an infrastructure may seem alien.

However, in order to make your business run smoothly, there are some basic building blocks that you must put in place, and some other processes that will really help you. It pays to get this right at the outset, but don't worry if you're a bit beyond that. It will still pay off to take stock of how you manage your business, and to make some changes where necessary.

Exercise 1 – nuts and bolts

Be clear what you need from a tangible, **physical** perspective. For most of us this includes a workspace, desk, chair, lighting, heating, notepads, pens, storage space ....

Think also about what you need that is specific to your business, e.g. if you keep written confidential customer records you will need a lockable cabinet.

Make a list and divide into two parts: the things you MUST have in place at outset, and those you can add later as you go along.

For example, you may be able to manage with an existing table and chair, but if you spend a lot of time at your desk you will need something more suitable before long or you will start to get aches and pains from sitting incorrectly.

Now	Later

Exercise 2 – technology

Consider what technology you need to run your business effectively. This will probably include a computer or laptop, a phone and broadband. It may also include a printer, a keyboard, a mouse, headphones and / or a separate microphone.

Think also about any technology you need that is specific to your business, e.g. software.

Once again, make a list and divide into two parts: the things you MUST have in place at outset, and those you can add later as you go along.

For example, you may be able to manage with an existing laptop at outset, but if it is old, slow or unreliable then you will need to plan to replace it before long.

Now	Later

Exercise 3 – infrastructure

It's important to ensure that your business is set up correctly and professionally. Some aspects will be relevant to all businesses, and there may be additional requirements specific to your industry, such as formal qualifications, legal processes, compliance or insurance.

The checklist below is a general one.

Make sure you have checked with your industry body and spoken to others in your industry to ensure you comply with industry specific requirements.

Topic	Detail	Action required
Legal	What's your legal framework – sole trader, limited company or partnership? If you have/will have employees there are a number of requirements to comply with.	
Compliance	This will depend on your legal framework, but make sure you have notified HMRC when you start your business even if you decide to be a sole trader (i.e. to regard yourself as self-employed for tax purposes). Also ensure you have registered with the Information Commissioner's Office (ICO) in relation to data protection.	

Topic	Detail	Action required
Banking	Do you need a separate bank account? If you have a limited company you definitely will. If you are a sole trader it's optional but strongly recommended.	
Insurance	What insurance do you need? In addition to industry specific insurance, think about: Home / office Contents / equipment Public liability Professional indemnity Employer's liability (if you have staff) Cyber	
Other	Are there any industry-specific requirements to comply with?	

Learning to take forward

What do you want to capture from these three exercises? Remember that the goal is to ensure you have a firm foundation for your business, with all the key structural building blocks in place.

Use this page to make some notes.

Bringing it all together

Congratulations on reaching this stage in the book.

By now, you have completed 27 exercises: 3 exercises for each of the 3 topics under each of the 3 big questions.

You should therefore have assembled Your Business Cube!

This means that:

- You know **WHY** you want to run a business, and why this business.

- You know **WHAT** your business looks like, and what you need to make it work.

- You know **HOW** you are going to make your business work for you.

I do hope you now have a better feel for the areas you already have sorted, and those you need to address in order to make your business a success. You will hopefully also have a better understanding of your personal definition of success.

You may also feel a little overwhelmed. We've covered a lot of ground and a lot of different topics. If so, this final question may help:

What are the three most important learnings that you are taking away?

Focus on these, and you will definitely move forward.

Still need some help?

I have a very special offer for you!

I am offering readers of my book a one-off 45-minute coaching session on Zoom for just £45.

I don't usually offer one-off sessions, so this is just for those of you who have read the book and would like to explore some aspect of it in a little more detail, or who would like my expert input in a particular area of your business.

To apply for this very special coaching offer, please contact me at amanda@businessmadesimpler.co.uk and put 'Business Cube coaching offer' in the heading.

As this offer is just for my readers, you'll be asked to answer three short questions about the book before I confirm your appointment.

Other ways to connect with me

If you'd like to hear more from me, I send out a FREE weekly newsletter every Tuesday, with insights, hints and tips. You can sign up to my newsletter here www.businessmadesimpler.co.uk/sign-up.

You can also follow me on Facebook at Business Made Simpler or on Twitter as @AmandaCcoach.

Or find me on LinkedIn. Send me an invitation to connect and mention this book and I'll be delighted to do so.

Finally, if you feel you need more 1:1 help than a one-off call, check out my coaching programmes on my website:

www.businessmadesimpler.co.uk/coaching

Thank you for coming on this journey with me. Good luck and I wish you every success with your business.

Amanda

About the Author

Amanda started her professional life as a pension consultant and spent more years than she cares to remember advising companies and trustee boards on running pension schemes for their members. She was a partner in a leading multinational consultancy where she combined business leadership with consulting to organisations large and small – many of them household names.

Along the way she faced lots of challenges, including navigating her way in a male-dominated world, merging and restructuring business units whilst treating all employees with respect and dignity, and striking a balance between confidence-inspiring leadership and approachability.

In 2012 Amanda decided it was time to change direction, so she retrained as a coach with the Coactive Training Institute, widely recognised as the gold standard in coach training. Soon afterwards she left the corporate world to set up her own coaching business. She now runs Business Made Simpler, delivering 1:1 coaching and workshops to owners of small businesses in the UK and beyond.

Amanda is married with one grown up daughter who also runs her own business – the entrepreneurial spirit runs in the family!

In her spare time Amanda enjoys doing puzzles, reading, gardening and dancing.

Contact the Author

Amanda can be contacted in the following ways:

Email: amanda@businessmadesimpler.co.uk

Website: www.businessmadesimpler.co.uk

Twitter: www.twitter.com/AmandaCcoach

Facebook: www.facebook.com/businessmadesimpler

LinkedIn: www.linkedin.com/in/amandacullencoach/

Printed in Great Britain
by Amazon

54742302R00047